iPhone 16 Us

A Comprehensive Guide to Using the New iPhone 16 Pro

& Pro Max: Step-by-Step Instructions for Seniors and

Novices with... Hints and Techniques

Chris Amber

1

Table of Contents

Introduction

Take a trip around the world of technical wonders with our in-depth manual, "iPhone 16 User Guide." This approachable handbook is international in scope, providing readers with a comprehensive understanding of the iPhone 16's marvels. Regardless of your level of experience with technology, this guide will help you make the most out of Apple's most recent flagship iPhone.

To assist you in utilizing the iPhone 16's features and functionalities, this guide offers detailed instructions and helpful hints. "iPhone 16 User Guide" has all the information you need to maximize the use of your smartphone, from configuring it to learning how to use the newest features and applications. You will be able to easily utilize the iPhone 16's power with the help of thorough explanations and illustrations. Thus, "iPhone 16

User Guide" contains all you need to improve productivity, take beautiful pictures, or just maintain relationships with loved ones. With the help of our in-depth guide, you can fully realize the potential of Apple's most recent flagship handset and improve your iPhone experience.

With "iPhone 16 User Guide," you'll have the skills and information necessary to utilize your iPhone 16 to its full potential wherever you are in the globe. This user-friendly manual will assist you in navigating and making use of all the features and capabilities of the iPhone 16, regardless of your level of technical expertise. Prepare to travel the world discovering technological wonders and improve your iPhone experience with our in-depth guide.

Important characteristics:

📱 *Examine Cutting-Edge Functionalities:* Explore the

cutting-edge features of the iPhone 16, including its sophisticated functionality and svelte form, and learn how it raises the bar for smartphones.

🌐 *Insights into Global Connectivity:* Recognize how the iPhone 16 guarantees uninterrupted worldwide connectivity, enabling you to stay connected wherever life may lead you.

🔍 *Comparisons with Rivals:* Make an informed choice by gaining knowledge from in-depth comparisons with major devices such as the Samsung Galaxy S23 Ultra, iPhone 11, iPhone 14, OnePlus 11, and iPhone 13.

🚀 *Evolutionary Timeline:* Follow the progression of the iPhone, starting with the iPhone 11 and ending with the iPhone 14, as well as the OnePlus 11, to see how the iPhone 16 evolved.

⚫ *Unlocked Freedom:* Discover the advantages of having an unlocked iPhone and look at models like the iPhone XR and iPhone SE, which provide unrivaled connectivity freedom all over the world.

📄 *Mastery of the Pro Max Series:* Improve your photographic abilities with the Pro Max series, which includes the most recent iPhone 14 Pro Max, iPhone 13 Pro Max, and iPhone 11 Pro Max.

🔒 *Privacy and Protection:* Make sure your data is safe by prioritizing privacy with accessories like the Speck iPhone 14 Pro Case and Privacy Screen iPhone 14 Plus.

🎧 *Sonic Excellence:* Upgrade your listening experience by immersing yourself in sonic splendor with accessories like Raycon Earbuds, Apple Headphones, and Apple AirPods Max.

⌚ *Wearable Tech Revolution:* Embrace the future with the Series 8, Series 9, Series 7, and Series 6 Apple Watches, which will effortlessly integrate into your daily activities and provide you with worldwide connectivity.

📺 *Entertainment Redefined:* With a look at Apple TV, Apple TV 4K 3rd Generation, and Apple TV Ultra, you can redefine your entertainment experience and enjoy a worldwide cinematic experience.

📡♂ *Fitness and Connectivity:* Adopt a healthy lifestyle with the Fuel Rod and Peloton Guide, accessories that will help you stay connected across the world and advance your fitness goals.

Why Opt for "iPhone 16 User Guide"?

This handbook has been painstakingly compiled to serve readers worldwide, guaranteeing:

🔐 *Security and Privacy:* With our insights into privacy accessories, arm yourself with the knowledge to protect your data.

🌐 *Global Adaptability:* Learn about the characteristics of the iPhone 16 that make it the ideal travel companion.

Skillful Navigation: Utilize the iPhone 16's sophisticated features with ease by following our comprehensive guides and professional advice.

Tech Literacy: Our tutorial fills in the knowledge gap, making the iPhone 16 User Guide approachable for users of all skill levels, whether they are tech enthusiasts or casual users.

Grab Your Copy Now to Immerse Yourself in the Greatest Smartphone Future!

Don't pass up this chance to master the iPhone 16. Get "iPhone 16 User Guide" now to improve your tech experience and become a part of the worldwide community of iPhone enthusiasts who have embraced the future!

Chapter 1

iPhone 16: Updates on the Price, Release Date, Specifications, and Additional Rumors

The iPhone 16 is the iPhone 15's inescapable replacement. This lineup is anticipated for late 2024 and may have Apple's own modem chip, larger screens, and the iPhone Ultra with Face ID embedded in the display.

When Is the iPhone 16 Coming Out?

Apple produces smartphones on a pretty consistent schedule, essentially ensuring a new model every year. The iPhone 16 won't be available until the next year, as the iPhone 15 was released this year.

Like in recent years, there will likely be multiple models:

12

iPhone 16, iPhone 16 Pro, iPhone 16 Pro Max, and possibly even an iPhone 16 Ultra.

Price rumors for the iPhone 16

Depending on the model and storage option you select, the price of an iPhone 15 can range from $799 to $1599. For now, we anticipate that similar costs will be repeated for the iPhone 16 in 2019.

Pre-Order Details

Soon after the phones are unveiled, you'll be able to place an order for the iPhone 16 on Apple's website. When a link is available, we'll post it here.

iPhone 16 Features & Specifications

The iPhone 16 Pro and Pro Max, according to Ross Young of Display Supply Chain Consultants, will feature larger 6.3-inch and 6.9-inch displays (the iPhone 14 Pro and Pro Max have 6.1-inch and 6.7-inch displays). Young hasn't said whether or if the iPhone 16 and iPhone 16 Plus will also have larger screens, so we'll have to wait for more details on those models' screen sizes.

In-display Face ID may be a feature of the 2024 iPhones, which could alter the design of the entire front of the phone. Should The Elec's story prove to be accurate, the iPhone Pro models may only come with the cutout for the front-facing camera:

With the upcoming iPhone 16 series Pro lineup, Apple is anticipated to implement the 'Under Panel Face ID' feature, which conceals Face ID beneath the screen.

As early as April 2022, Ming-Chi Kuo, a writer and frequent leaker on Apple, predicted this same rumor.

However, reliable leaker Ross Young believes that under-panel Face ID will be delayed until at least 2025 and consequently launch alongside the iPhone 17 Pro because of sensor problems. If he is correct, the overall appearance of the 2024 phones will undoubtedly be inspired by the iPhone 15 series (all models will feature the Dynamic Island cutout).

Better zoom capabilities are anticipated if this phone includes a periscope camera lens. Beginning in early 2023, Kuo revealed that the results of his most recent poll "indicates only one/highest-end new iPhone 16 model in 2H24 will have the periscope camera." This rumor is most likely in reference to the iPhone Ultra.

The iPhone 16 is expected to feature a vertical camera setup, just like the iPhone 12. A 48MP super wide-angle lens is also anticipated to be included with the iPhone 16 Pro and Pro Max phones (the iPhone 14 Pro models feature a 12MP ultra wide-angle lens).

There are now four storage options for the iPhone,

ranging from 128 GB to TB. Since a 2 TB model is not yet anticipated, we believe the iPhone 16 will keep things the same. Although it's still improbable, we could see Apple abandoning the entry-level model and instead starting with 256 GB.

Although Apple has long utilized Qualcomm modem chips in their phones, it may begin using its own modem chip in 2024. It's unclear what the buyer would gain from this, if anything.

Wi-Fi 7 is expected to be upgraded in the iPhone 16, according to Kuo, who also notes that it "will be more conducive to Apple's integration of hardware products running on the same local network and provide a better ecosystem experience."

The operating system that comes pre-installed on the iPhone 16 will be iOS 18. After iOS 17 is confirmed, we'll know more about what to expect in that operating system.

The low-light sensitivity of the iPhone 16 Pro cameras may be doubled.

Although the 48MP stacked sensor technology used in the iPhone 14 Pro and Pro Max is anticipated to be included in all four iPhone 15 models, the iPhone 16 Pro cameras from the next year may once more outperform the entry-level and Plus models.

While the specifics of a recent supply chain report are unclear, it appears to hint at a new Sony technology that roughly doubles the low-light sensitivity.

The iPhone 14 and iPhone 15 include stacked sensors.

Apple resisted the urge to follow in the footsteps of Samsung and other companies who have long pursued cameras with impressive-sounding megapixel counts.

17

This is due to the fact that packing a large number of pixels into a tiny sensor has a significant drawback: lower low-light performance due to the high pixel density.

Apple's use of a stacked sensor, which has numerous layers to keep low-light sensitivity, was the final solution to that challenge. This year, the whole iPhone 15 lineup is anticipated to include the technology that was initially included in the two iPhone 14 Pro models.

New sensors to be used in iPhone 16 Pro cameras

The most recent report from Ming-Chi Kuo is incredibly vague, but it does reveal that the two iPhone 16 Pro variants will have different sensors than the standard models and that Sony will once again be the supplier of the sensors.

Note: Sony's high-end CIS capacity will be constrained

in 2024 since two 2H24 iPhone 16 Pro models will also use stacked-designed CIS.

The article focuses on a rival of Sony and mentions that Semi will get more orders from Android firms since Apple will be utilizing the majority of Sony's smartphone sensor output.

possibly a sign of bigger photo diodes

Although the article doesn't specify which Sony stacked sensor technology will be utilized in the iPhone 16 Pro cameras, we can speculate.

With Sony's most recent stacked sensor technology, the traditionally integrated photo diodes and pixel transistors are separated. As a result, for a given total pixel size, the photo diodes—the part that actually collects light—can be much larger.

Moving the diodes to a different layer allows both to be

larger, as explained in a recent Sony promotional video (below), which eliminates the need to place them next to the transistors, which would have limited their size. Accordingly, more light is captured by the diodes and more noise is eliminated by the transistors.

Roughly twice as much light is captured, according to Sony.

This is in contrast to the usual trend where new camera sensor technology appears first in high-end cameras and then cellphones. The Sony Xperia 1 V smartphone is the first known device to use the technology. According to Digital Camera World, scalability issues may be the reason of this.

You may also be wondering why Sony is showcasing this revolutionary sensor technology in a camera phone rather than a possible flagship camera such as the A9 III or A1 II. If we were to speculate, it's probable that existing manufacturing procedures are limited to making physically small sensor chips, given the cited technological constraints in producing a dual-layer sensor. It might take longer to scale the technique up to full-frame sensor size.

How will this affect images taken on an iPhone?

In two common scenarios, higher light and noise levels translate into better images.

First, dim lighting. Taking pictures inside of restaurants at night is a prime illustration of how many establishments purposefully keep lighting dim to create a sophisticated and romantic ambiance. However, a lot of pictures of infants and young children are also taken indoors, and low light levels might occur at home, particularly during the winter.

Second, lighting with strong contrast. The classic

illustration of this is outside in direct sunshine, where there is a significant dynamic range, or difference in light levels between places that receives sun and shadow. Another typical example is shooting into the light; consider taking a picture of someone against a sunset.

These two scenarios have long been a top priority for Apple and Sony, so if this technology is included in the iPhone 16 Pro cameras, we should anticipate another very significant advancement the following year.

With the release of the iPhone 16 Pro, In-Display Face ID will finally be available.

Face ID took the place of Touch ID on Apple's flagship devices with the release of the iPhone X in 2017. With the iPhone 13 series, it began with a notch that got smaller. With the iPhone 14 Pro models, Apple did away with the notch in favor of the Dynamic Island, and it appears that they will continue to do so in the years to come. Without a doubt, the Dynamic Island cutout on the front will be there on the entire iPhone 15 series. It has been reported that the iPhone 16 Pro versions for the upcoming year would have an in-display Face ID system.

The in-display camera will be included with the iPhone 18 Pro, although the iPhone 16 Pro will include an in-display Face ID mechanism.

According to The Elec, Apple has the technology to enable light to flow through the glass screen of the iPhone and into the TrueDepth camera configuration for in-display Face ID. Should this story hold any weight, the iPhone 16 Pro variants may only include the cutout for the front-facing camera. In addition to providing consumers with extra screen real estate, the display above the TrueDepth camera system would function normally.

Apple is not the first company to do this kind of approach. Samsung has been experimenting with under-display technologies for some time, and the current Galaxy Z Fold series is the result. Similar to Samsung's solution, Apple's in-display Face ID will use pixels to hide up the TrueDepth sensors that are buried beneath the display.

According to the source, Apple plans to remove in-display Face ID from the regular iPhone models by 2025. Apple has established a distinction between the "Pro" and "standard" iPhone models and will continue to do so in future iterations. Apple will now provide the iPhone 18 Pro versions with an in-display camera system. This indicates that the iPhone 'Pro' models from 2026 will be the first to feature a distraction-free all-screen display.

Apple has guaranteed a special place for the "Pro" iPhone models, which come with extra hardware enhancements and unique functionality. For example, the ordinary models of the iPhone 14 retain the design from the iPhone 13, but the Pro variants sport the new Dynamic Island cutout. The two-year cycle is a significant factor in the iPhone display refresh. Up to the all-screen feature, every iPhone will come with enhanced display technology for a period of two years.

We have previously heard information about the in-display Face ID and camera configuration. The same information was given by Ross Young back in 2022, pointing out that the iPhone 16 Pro will have Face ID under the display, while the iPhone 18 Pro will have an in-display camera by 2026. When do you think Apple will release an all-screen iPhone model? Share your opinions with us in the comments section.

Chapter 2

iOS 16

Among the many improvements of the iOS 16 upgrade are the customization of the lock screen, text editing and unsending capabilities, and much more.

Date of Release for iOS 16

On September 12, Apple released iOS 16, continuing its lengthy history of iOS updates. June saw the debut of iOS 16 at WWDC 2022.

The simplest method to download the iOS update wirelessly is to go to Settings > General > Software Update if your phone is compatible with iOS 16 (a list of compatible devices is provided below).

Cost of iOS 16

Updates for iOS are always free! While not all phones are able to install it (see below), there is no cost for those that can.

Features of iOS 16

It was originally anticipated that the iCloud shared photo library functionality would be included in the initial release of iOS 16, but it has been postponed to a later version.

The following are a some of the more notable adjustments:

- Schedules and filters for focus: There are situations in which a Focus can activate automatically, such as when you're using a particular app or place. For instance, when you're in work mode, several Safari tabs may open.

- Customizing the lock screen: In addition to

changing the typeface and elemental positions, you can add widgets and Live Activities to the iOS 16 lock screen, as well as associate the lock screen with a Focus. You have the ability to quickly switch between multiple lock screens that you have built.

- Battery percentage: Rather than using a visual indicator to show the battery level, Apple has changed the battery symbol on iPhones with Face ID to show a percentage figure.

- Edit and unsend text messages: iMessage now offers this feature, which is supported by many other messaging apps. Even after a message has been sent, it is still possible to amend it. You can make changes up to five times per message, and previous edits will be visible in a history log. You have two minutes to delete a text message (ten seconds if it's an email).

- Shared Tab Groups: As friends shut and open tabs, you may work together in real time while sharing groups of Safari tabs.

- Live Text: Simply extract text from paused photos or videos and respond to it instantaneously, for example, to follow shipments or translate text. Siri modifications: With iOS 16, Siri can handle additional offline requests, conclude FaceTime calls on your behalf, and send messages without asking for permission.

- Enhancements in accessibility: The Apple Watch can be fully controlled from an iPhone, and automatic live captions are available for audio, video, and conversations, including FaceTime video chats. Magnifier mode can recognize persons and doors to read signs or labels.

- Tracking health apps: To maintain a complete picture of your consistency, make a list of all the prescriptions you take and record the times you take them on your phone. Additionally, you'll find out whether there are any worries regarding drug interactions.

- Passwords for WiFi in Settings: Settings is where you may view, share, and remove saved Wi-Fi passwords.

- Safety Check: This new function is being introduced by the Settings app to assist you in some scenarios where you need to rapidly revoke the access you've granted to other individuals.

- SharePlay via Messaging: Instantaneously share media files, games, movies, and more with contacts via Messages.

Supported Devices for iOS 16

With the exception of the iPhone SE 1st generation, iPhone 6S, and iPhone 7, if your phone can run iOS 15, it can also run iOS 16.

Apart from the devices mentioned above, iOS 16 is compatible with the following devices:

- iPhone Pro Max (version 11 and up)

- iPhone Pro (version 11 and up)

- iPhone models 11 and above

- iPhone mini 12 and later models

- iPhone SE (version 2 and later)

- iPhone X and XR

- iPhone XS and XS Max

- iPhone 8 and 8 Plus

How to Utilize iPhone Live Activities (iOS 16)

With Live Activities, you can quickly access information and features from compatible apps directly from your lock screen. You may use them without having to unlock your iPhone or open the apps themselves.

You must be running iOS 16 or later in order to use Live Activities. As said, Live Activities on the iPhone 14 Pro and Pro Max also utilize the area provided by the Dynamic Island.

To activate live activities on an iPhone, take the following actions:

- Select Settings.

- Touch Passcode & Face ID.

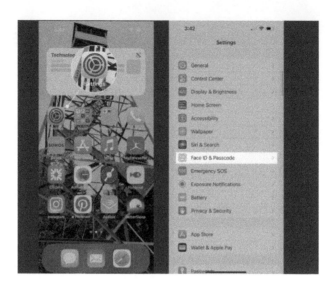

- Put in your passcode here.

- Slide the Live Activities slider to the on/green position in the Allow Access while Locked section.

Depending on the apps you use, different Live Activities may be available in them and different methods for activating them. A Live Activity may be removed from your lock screen simply sliding it from right to left.

Advice: You may configure Live Activities on iPhones running iOS 16.2 and later to update sports results more regularly. To begin with, make sure this option is enabled in Settings > TV > Live Activities by moving the sliders for Allow Live Activities and More Frequent Updates to the green or on positions. Next, select the game from the TV app's detail screen by tapping it and selecting Follow. Your lock screen's Live Activity for that game is updated often.

Live activities: What Are They?

You can add Live Activities to your iPhone lock screen to get a little glimpse into an app that updates information on a regular basis. They enable an app to quickly display important information that you'll need, such as the score of a sporting event, the location of your food delivery, the current weather, and more.

As their name implies, Live Activities are updated often and provide essential information that can be accessed without launching an app by simply glancing at your screen (perfect with the iPhone 14's always-on screen).

Consider them to be interactive lock screen widgets or notifications that refresh almost instantly.

Live Events Compatible with iPhone 14 Pro and Up

36

Not only does Live Activities leverage the Dynamic Island on the iPhone 14 Pro and Pro Max to deliver updates as you use other apps, but it also does it from the lock screen. In these models, data is always present in the Dynamic Island in a collapsed form. Occasionally, the Dynamic Island enlarges to display a very significant item, and you can press the Dynamic Island to open that application.

When you're listening to a song in Music, for instance, the Dynamic Island displays a thumbnail of the album art, and tapping the image opens the album in Music. Another example would be the Dynamic Island displaying the team logos and the current score while you're watching a sporting event. The Dynamic Island enlarges to display the outcome when the game is finished.

Applications to Facilitate Live Events

There are a few dozen, maybe two hundred, apps that support Live Activities as of this writing. It would be impossible to include them all here due to their sheer number, but you may find some excellent choices by searching for "live activities" or "dynamic island" in the App Store.

Pre-installed apps on the iPhone that can be used for Live Activities, Dynamic Island updates, or both are as follows:

- Clock (for timers)

- Voice Memos; TV; Music; Maps.

How to Use iOS 16 to Lock a Hidden Photo Album on an iPhone

Photos on your iPhone vanish from your camera roll when you conceal them. Still present on your phone, though—they're simply in the Hidden album. Anyone with access to your phone can still view these hidden photos by opening the Hidden album, unless you lock it down. If you wish to lock the hidden folder using one of those methods, your smartphone must support Face ID or Touch ID. This security feature requires iOS 16 or later.

On your iPhone, follow these steps to lock hidden photos:

- Select Photos after opening Settings.

- To activate it, tap the Use Touch ID or Use Face ID toggle.

- You can also choose to disable it by tapping the Show Hidden Album toggle.

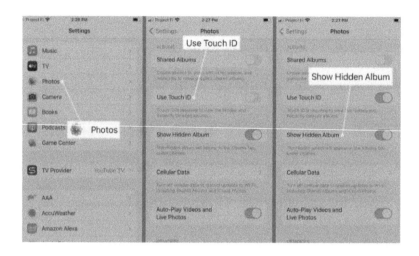

Note: If you wish to keep the existence of your concealed images on your phone a secret, use this setting.

How to Check and See iPhone's Locked Hidden Pictures

Open the Photos app to confirm that your secret album is indeed shut down. As long as you didn't decide to remove the album from the album list, it will still be there. However, in order to view the images, you'll need to utilize Touch ID or Face ID.

Note: You will be required to enter your passcode to unlock the album after many unsuccessful Touch ID or Face ID tries. By employing that strategy, anyone with access to your passcode will be able to view your concealed images.

To confirm that your secret album is locked, follow these steps:

- Once the Photos app is open, select Albums.

- Under Utilities, look for lock symbols next to Recently Deleted and Hidden.

- Tap Hidden to see your hidden pictures.

- After selecting View Album, you can unlock the

folder with Touch ID or Face ID.

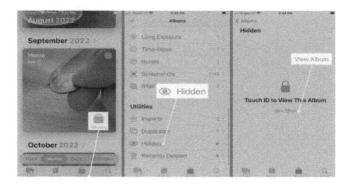

Why Do iPhone Photos Get Locked?

For a limited time, you can choose to hide images on your iPhone by moving them from the camera roll into the Hidden album. If all you want a picture to be out of the main camera roll, that's okay, but it doesn't really stop others from viewing it. There is nothing stopping someone from going to your Hidden album and viewing pictures you didn't want them to see if you give them access to your phone so they may look at some of your shots.

You can choose to conceal the Hidden album in the

Photos app so that it doesn't appear in your album listing. That's useful since it keeps your hidden photos from being discovered, but it doesn't truly prevent people from seeing them. Even if your Hidden album doesn't appear alongside your other albums, someone with the right skills can find and view it with ease.

In other respects, the concealed album falls short of safeguarding your concealed photos. For instance, you can pull photographs from the Hidden folder while using the image picker in other apps to select images.

With iOS 16, came the ability to lock your Hidden album, which effectively safeguards your hidden pictures. Your Hidden album is locked behind Touch ID or Face ID when this functionality is enabled. A blank folder appears to anyone who attempts to view the Hidden album without your authorization. In the same way, this feature secures your recently erased photos.

This option safeguards your hidden photographs outside of the Photos app in addition to locking them down inside of it. Neither the picture picker in other apps nor any third-party apps will be able to access hidden images.

How to Utilize an iPhone's Photo Cutout feature (iOS 16)

With photo altering software like Photoshop, removing a person or object from a backdrop image so you might utilize it in another setting used to be a difficult task. Over time, such tools have made it easier, and now that iOS 16 brought a capability to the iPhone, doing it on your phone is quite simple. It only requires a few taps.

To utilize Photo Cutout to exclude an individual or object from its background, follow these steps:

- Tap the picture in the Photos app to make it the only image shown on your screen.

- To remove a person or object from a photo, tap and hold it.

Note: We occasionally have to repeat this in our testing. You can proceed to the next stage if you experience haptic feedback. Remove your finger from the screen and try again if you are unable to feel it on the first attempt.

- The borders of what will be cropped out of the picture are indicated by the light outline that surrounds the person or object that the Photos app recognized. There's a pop-up menu.

- Once the object is selected, you have two options: you can share it with another app or copy it (for the latter, go to the following step).

- To transfer the picture to the clipboard on your iPhone, tap transfer. Then, using the same method as copying and pasting text, you can paste it into another app.

- To directly share the selected object with another app, tap Share. To add an object to an app, simply tap it from the sharing pane that appears.

- The cut-out item is now usable for editing, sending by text or email, and more, with whatever capabilities and settings are available in the app you added it to, regardless of whether you copied or shared it.

Note: The border denoting the object selection cannot be altered. In our tests, the iPhone nearly always accurately depicted the perimeter of a person or object without omitting crucial information or incorporating unnecessary things. It did, however, make a few mistakes, and there is currently no way to change what is included.

Visual Lookup Is the Basis for Photo Cutout

The Visual Lookup technology, which Apple debuted with iOS 15, serves as the foundation for Photo Cutout.

Through the use of Visual Lookup, the iPhone can identify and interact with things that are displayed in photos. That originally meant things like text in a photo being copyable or identifying a phone number in a snapshot of a sign and enabling you to contact that number with a single press. That still functions, naturally.

With Photo Cutout, Apple expanded those capabilities to include object or human detection. Essentially, the idea is the same: an iPhone "looks" at a picture, "understands" what's in it, and then lets you do things with the items—in this example, slicing them out of a background and pasting them into other apps.

Note: While Portrait Mode currently separates subject and backdrop, Photo Cutout might perform a little better with certain types of shots; however, in our testing, it performed well with a wide range of photos.

Not Every Compatible iPhone Can Use Every iOS 16

Feature: What You Should Know

The latest version of Apple's iOS 16, which is compatible with the iPhone X and subsequent models, has certain capabilities that are exclusive to owners of the latest models. This is something that experts believe Apple could not have avoided.

While the majority of iOS 16's features are compatible with all compatible iPhone models, two accessibility features, for example, cannot be used on any iPhone model older than model year. Those whose iPhones don't make the cut will have to upgrade in order to enjoy iOS 16 in its entirety, but experts think Apple made the correct decision in this case—and it may not have had much of a choice.

"Unfortunately, it appears that certain features are restricted by hardware," revealed Carolina Milanesi, Creative Strategies' President & Principal Analyst, in an email. She went on to say, "The processing power or AI/Machine Learning capabilities are just not all the same," implying that some functions are simply insufficient on older devices.

Absent Aspects

Though short, the list of features that new iPhones must have is not without its highlights. One notable feature that Apple showcased at its iOS 16 launching event in

June is still absent: the capability to extract objects and people from a photograph and reposition them elsewhere. According to Apple, in order to utilize that feature, users must have a "iPhone with A12 Bionic and later," therefore those with the iPhone XS or later model can proceed, but those with an older model cannot.

For two accessibility aspects, the narrative is likewise comparable. A brand-new dictation tool that automatically punctuates text as users speak is part of the iOS 16 upgrade. Emojis are even supported for the first time, however the new dictation engine's on-device functionality necessitates an iPhone with the A12 Bionic chip or later. Once more, users of iPhone X and iPhone 8 are excluded.

When it comes to FaceTime calls and other live content that has captions added, things get trickier with Live Captions. According to Apple, either an iPad with the

A12 Bionic or an iPhone 11 or later—a device that employs the A13 Bionic—is necessary. But it's unclear from Apple's documentation why the iPad may use the outdated processor.

Apple has a track record of providing lengthy support for outdated devices, often issuing many iOS feature updates even after an iPhone is discontinued. Recently, the corporation also published a security fix for iPhones that are nine years old. For purchasers of secondhand iPhones as well as iPhone users, a lengthy backlog of security and feature updates prolongs the useful life of the device. Additionally, it's more environmentally friendly than everyone purchasing a new iPhone every year.

Experts say that's not at all the case if someone thinks Apple withholds features to entice users to switch to a new iPhone. Independent software developer Martin Pilkington thinks it's only a matter of technological advancement, citing the A12 Bionic as an example. He revealed via direct chat that "all these AI/Machine Learning features would need it as a minimum requirement because the A12's Neural Engine was more flexible and powerful."

However, not everything makes sense; the Live Caption function of iOS 16 is one such instance. Why is the iPad's A12 Bionic capable of handling the feature, while the iPhone XS's A12 Bionic is unable to? Declaring that "the A12 Bionic in the iPad is the same as the one in the iPhone XS," Pilkington expresses his uncertainty, adding that "if anything, it's weaker as the iPhone XS has more

RAM [than the iPad]."

Regretfully, the feature in question is Live Captions, an accessibility tool that many have praised as "amazing" and their "favorite feature" of the software upgrade.

How iOS 16 Allows You to Personalize an iPhone Lockscreen

You have access to a whole new range of iPhone customization options if your device is running iOS 16 or later. You may now modify your lock screen in addition to the numerous customization options available in earlier iOS versions. This is how you do it:

- Long-press the lock screen on your iPhone.

- Press the blue plus sign.

- You must choose a new wallpaper if you're using an old one. In the pop-up menu, select Add New.

- From the Add New Wallpaper screen, select a new wallpaper.

- Tap it to change the day and date. Select fonts and colors from the pop-up menu located at the bottom of the screen.

Note: The lock screen's day and date section allows you to install one widget. You can just drag and drop a widget there.

- Tap it to change the time. Select fonts and colors from the pop-up menu located at the bottom of the screen.

- Widgets are available for the lock screen. Four little widgets, two medium widgets, or one medium and two small widgets are available for selection. Click the + next to the time to accomplish that.

o To add a widget to the lock screen, simply tap on it or them. Additionally, you can drag and drop them into the widget section.

o Widgets can be dragged to change where they are shown.

o After adding a widget to the lock screen, you can delete it by tapping its - icon.

Tips: Homescreen widgets and lock screen widgets are comparable: They are updated on a regular basis to display fresh data, and clicking on them opens the program that is linked to the widget.

• To apply either Perspective Zoom or Depth Effects to your lock screen, tap the... symbol.

• Once you've made all the customizations you desire and are prepared to save and utilize it, select Done.

Using Several Lock Screens on iOS 16 and Later

You can choose to store each customized lock screen as a separate option at any time. Use these methods to access lock screens that are already in place and change a few other settings:

- Press and hold the lock screen.

- View all of the lock screens you've made by swiping side to side.

- To associate a lock screen with a Focus state, select a preset Focus setting by tapping Focus.

Tips: This lets you have a lock screen with lots of helpful widgets in the Focus option for when you want to be accessible, and a lock screen that just shows the time and day when you want to concentrate on work or sleep.

- To activate the lock screen, simply tap on the

desired screen.

Method for Removing Lock Screens

Here's how to remove a personalized lock screen that already exists:

- Press and hold the lock screen.

- To remove a lock screen, swipe left or right to locate it.

- To erase the lock screen, long press on it.

- Select "Delete Wallpaper."

Physical security keys are supported in iOS 16.3, but they might not be required.

You will soon be able to use a real key to secure your iCloud login.

Apple has included support for hardware security keys in

the most recent iterations of iOS 16. These are similar to digital replicas of real keys in that you need to insert the key into your device in order to verify yourself in order to connect into iCloud or your Apple ID. Furthermore, you become locked out if you misplace the key, much like in the real world. There is a significant decrease in convenience and a large increase in security. So, the issue is: Is the trouble worth it?

"The most secure kind of two-factor authentication is a physical security key. Naturally, two-factor authentication and password managers are crucial cybersecurity support features. Amir Tarighat, privacy expert and CEO of cybersecurity startup Agency, revealed via email that a physical security key goes even further, adding a third layer of authentication that prevents bad actors from accessing your files, data, sensitive information, etc., if they don't have the actual, physical key.

An Additional Factor

Authentication techniques are frequently divided into groups in the context of passwords and security. Something you possess, like a physical key; something you know, like a password; and something you are, like a fingerprint or facial scan.

If this were a movie scene, you could have to enter a passcode, scan an ID card, and also scan your palm or retina in order to enter a high-security building.

However, in reality, these distinctions are frequently hazy. Your phone may use a Face ID scan to authenticate to the keychain, but after that, it will just enter your password for the website or app. Additionally, using a two-factor authenticator like Google Authenticator or Authy requires that you have access to your physical device, but occasionally these apps can sync across many devices.

Nevertheless, the key idea here is that the more of these areas you have covered, the more difficult it will be to access any of your accounts.

Key to Security

Security keys have long been compatible with desktop, laptop, and mobile computers. The distinction lies in the fact that you will be able to utilize one to access your Apple ID starting with iOS 16.3 in 2023.

Once you sign into iCloud on one of your devices, you'll need it, but after that, it's finished. If you employ the device-to-device transfer process during setup, your authentication will remain intact even if you get a new iPad or iPhone.

However, as Apple will not produce its own keys, you will need to purchase one from a third-party vendor. Depending on your needs, the key may be USB-C,

Lightning, or NFC. Of course, you should perform extensive research on the vendor if you're concerned about security. Otherwise, what's the point?

The inability of a physical key to be phished is its greatest benefit. No matter how skilled the attacker is or how advanced the phishing campaign is, they cannot access your account unless they take the real key from you.

Hassle vs. Security

Is all of this worth the hassle, then? Most likely not. You can probably be sure it's a business issue if you witness someone utilizing one of these keys. If a company doesn't want its employees to fall victim to phishing, it might require them to utilize a security key in order to access company servers.

You can be certain that even in the unlikely event that

someone managed to figure out your password, they would still be unable to access your account if you use a physical security key. Stated differently, having physical security keys makes it considerably more difficult for hackers to access your accounts," technology columnist Rick Costa revealed through email.

In your situation, you most likely already know whether or not you want to use a security key to protect your Apple ID. Do you believe there's a chance the government may attempt to access the data on your iCloud account? Are the security measures in place insufficient?

Together with Apple's other recent security updates for your iCloud account, like Advanced Data Protection, which encrypts practically all of your iCloud data on Apple servers so that not even Apple can access it, comes this new hardware function. Upon activating it, you will be required to create and record a 28-character Recovery Key, which you ought to keep secure.

Alternatively, you can designate a recovery contact that will assist you in getting back into your account. A hacker, however, sees an additional attack vector to take advantage of when one person sees a reliable friend.

The trade-off ultimately comes down to convenience vs security. This may go too far from the "convenience" side for a lot of folks, but for others, Apple's new security features may be ideal.

The Canine Removal Mode on iOS 16 Is Far More Beneficial Than You May Imagine

The 'dog-extraction' mode, also known as the cutout tool, is one of the most amazing features of iOS 16 and is also quite useful. It's not just for dog photos, either.

Try this if your iPhone is running iOS 16: Launch the

Photos app and select a photo that catches your eye, preferably one that features a person. After that, tap that person, wait for the magical ripple effect to emerge, and then drag. That individual was simply pulled out of the backdrop by you! "The new dog extraction mode in iOS 16 is not just for dog lovers. It has a few great uses, both serious and fun. The effect is instantaneous and powerful." It can be used to highlight a subject and draw attention to them in a picture. Regular users who are not familiar with photoshopping software or those who need to quickly modify their images for social media posting or even professional or work-related use will find this ideal." Technology writer and TechRT co-founder Rajesh Namase revealed via email.

Stop It Now

It doesn't seem like this new tool has an official name. Although the popup menu item is labeled "Lift subject from background," some design sites prefer to refer to it as "dog-extraction mode," citing an illustration provided by Apple during the feature's demo. Other sites, like this one, prefer the term "cutout tool."

However you refer to it, it is really awesome. To use an object, person, or animal anywhere else in an image, you merely need to drag it out. Given that dragging between windows will be easier on the iPad and Mac when iPadOS 16 and macOS Ventura launch later this year, it does appear that this could be a little more helpful on both platforms. However, it's still fantastic on the iPhone right now, and you can copy the extracted item to the clipboard for subsequent copying if you'd like. The majority of built-in apps that display images and iPhones with an A12 chip or later support these functionalities.

A large portion of my previous work as a graphic designer involves cutting things out of images. I once had to manually extract every single phone image by drawing around it in a book I designed about the history of cellphones. Although Photoshop now offers image-separating capabilities of its own, Apple's is remarkable in terms of both speed and strength.

Photoshop, however, continues to do far better.

Professional graphic designer Graham Bower revealed via email that "I think the cutout is a great bit of fun, but not useful for professional designers." "It's intriguing, though; it's difficult to replicate the way it handles fluffy fur. It is a very good feature. Very enjoyable, but completely unrelated to graphic designers in the field."

Moods and Stickers

What then is this useful for? Turning the pictures into stickers is now one of the more entertaining possibilities. A few apps are currently available that will take the extracted image from the clipboard and create a sticker with a drop shadow and a white or colored border that can be used in the Messages app.

According to Bower, "They do look great as stickers."

Those who frequently create mood boards and look books using web photos may find another application for them. For instance, a fashion stylist can swiftly merge multiple scenes together or remove individuals from backdrops to create a more minimalist feel.

You can also take the item out of the background if you're selling items online through classified advertisements, leaving just the sofa visible to potential buyers.

Using it on images taken in iPhone portrait mode is one way to get better cutouts. These include depth information that is typically used to obfuscate the backdrop, but it also produces far cleaner extractions based on my testing.

Chapter 3

Options That Are Best for Restoring iPhone Screens

Everyone falls their iPhone or even iPod touch every now and then. The results of most falls aren't serious, however, in some instances, screens break or shatter. A few of these splits are minor aesthetic issues that don't hinder using your gadget. Others are therefore extensive that it becomes very difficult to see the display screen or use the iPhone.

Plenty of companies offer you low-cost iPhone display repair or display screen alternative but beware: If you're not careful, you can find yourself voiding your guarantee from Apple and dropping all the assistance and benefits it includes.

iPhone Screen Fix Costs If You Are Under Warranty

The typical iPhone warranty doesn't protect against accidental damage, meaning Apple doesn't offer cracked iPhone screen repair in the warranty.

Take note: It's essential to understand that the iPhone guarantee says that when the iPhone will be fixed by anyone apart from an Apple-authorized technology, the entire guarantee is voided. Practically all from the low-cost restoration shops aren't Apple authorized, therefore saving money together can make you lose your guarantee.

If you want a screen fix or replace, start checking whether your iPhone is under warranty. If it's, you may get assistance directly from Apple company, go directly to the mobile phone company you purchased the telephone from, or make use of an Apple-authorized reseller.

One nice reward of having Apple company fix your cell phone is that Apple company stores may replace iPhone displays and never have to send your cell phone out for support, so you'll receive your telephone back in zero time.

Fixing a Damaged iPhone Screen When You Have AppleCare

The situation may be the same when you have an AppleCare warranty. Going to Apple company for the iPhone screen restoration is a lot more essential since utilizing an unauthorized repair center will void your regular guarantee as well as the AppleCare guarantee.

Unlike the typical iPhone warranty, AppleCare addresses two incidents of accidental damage, with a charge for each fix. This cost is probably a lot more than what an unauthorized repair center will charge, nonetheless it keeps your guarantee and means that your restoration is conducted by individuals best trained to accomplish it.

Fixing a Damaged iPhone Screen When You Have iPhone Insurance

If you purchased iPhone insurance coverage through your mobile phone company or by yourself, you need to consult with your insurance company to comprehend their guidelines around screen maintenance. Most iPhone insurance policy covers accidental harm. Based on your plan, you might have to cover a deductible along with a restoration charge, but that combo could be less than changing the iPhone completely.

You should choose to have an iPhone insurance plan, though, be sure to get all of the facts and charges before investing in using your insurance coverage, as many people complain about bad encounters if they use an insurance policy for these kinds of repairs.

iPhone Screen Maintenance In Case Your iPhone has

gone out of Warranty

If you don't have a guarantee or insurance plan for your cell phone, you've got more options. In cases like this, a low-cost repair center might be a good choice since it can save you cash. If you don't have a guarantee or AppleCare, you might have less to reduce by using one of these brilliant shops.

It's a good concept to work with a store that's familiar with iPhone display, repair and contains a good status. Even though they can not violate a guarantee that's expired, an unskilled restoration person might lead to additional harm to the body or electronics panel of one's iPhone. That could cause more actual problems and may cause you to have to buy a new phone.

Fixing a Damaged iPhone Display If You're Qualified to receive an Upgrade

If you've paid to swap your iPhone to buy a new one, if

you've use your iPhone for a lot more than 2 yrs, or would consider returning to a fresh phone company, you might be qualified to receive a discounted upgrade to a more recent model. A damaged screen may be an excellent motivator for an upgrade.

If you choose to upgrade, browse the companies that purchase used iPhones. They also buy types with broken displays, to change your old phone into supplemental income.

Preventing iPhone Screen from Harm in the foreseeable future

There's simply no foolproof technique for preventing harm to iPhone displays. If your telephone drops and abuse, ultimately actually the best-protected iPhone will split. Still, several easy steps can decrease the likelihood of damaged displays. Use:

Instances: Some situations offer display screen

protection, quite a few don't. Even though the situation you possess doesn't add a display protector, the situation itself provides some safety that may reduce the chance of damaging the display. Have a look at our picks to discover the best iPhone cases.

Display screen Protectors: This slim, plastic material overlays generally protect the display screen from scratches or dings, however, they provide a little additional defense against splits, too. Most instance is an even more comprehensive answer, but screen protectors are good add-ons.

AppleCare: For the next mobile phone, consider purchasing AppleCare if you didn't before. It adds a little to your current cost, but it is almost always worth it to obtain two full many years of support and maintenance from trained specialists.

Can't Get Apps on Your iPhone? 11 Ways

to Make It Better

It could be incredibly frustrating whenever your iPhone won't download apps. In the end, applications are part of the actual iPhone, so excellent. No matter whether you're aiming to download new applications or update applications you currently have, you want this to work. Fortunately, fixing this issue is not too difficult.

Why Does the iPhone Not Allow Apps to Install?

While mending an iPhone that won't download applications is not too difficult, what can cause the problem isn't quite so simple. Actually, there are almost as much potential factors behind this mistake as there are fixes for this. These range between App Store guidelines to simple insects, from issues with your Apple ID to your iPhone's configurations and more. Instead of providing a summary of the causes here, each solution below provides some history for the problem.

77

Solutions for iPhones That Won't Download Apps

If applications won't download to your iPhone, try these fixes, in this order.

- Try Wi-Fi. If you are aiming to download the application more than a mobile connection like 4G LTE, you may be hitting a restriction of the App Store. Apple limitations how big is app downloading over mobile to 150 MB. That is done to avoid users from using too much data about the same download. If the application you want to download is bigger than that, hook up to Wi-Fi. It is also smart to check to ensure you are not in Airplane Setting, which blocks all Wi-Fi and mobile network connections.

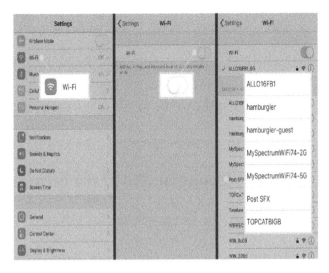

- Restart the App Store app. The insect in installing the app may need to do with the App Store application itself. If something will go wrong with this app, it will not have the ability to help set up the application you want. If so, restarting the App Store application may clear the insect. Then, just re-open the App Store application and make an effort to re-download the app.

- Pause and restart the application download. This suggestion only works on devices with a 3D Touchscreen (the iPhone 6S and newer, aside from the iPhone XR). It works whenever your application download has been interfered with for reasons unknown. If an application icon shows up on your home display, however the download seems sluggish or like it isn't occurring, hard press the icon for the application you're trying to set up. In the menu that pops right out of the icon, faucet Resume Download (whether it's already paused). You can do the same thing in the App Store app, on the display screen for the application you want to set up.

• Restart iPhone. Exactly like restarting the App Store application can solve the issue of apps not installing on your iPhone, sometimes you will need to restart all of your phone. This may be because the short-term glitch in your telephone could maintain the operating-system or another area of the phone's software. A restart will most likely resolve that type of issue.

- Check your Apple ID payment methods. To be able to download apps, you must have a payment method on document in your Apple ID. That is true even if you are aiming to download a free of charge app. So, unless you have a payment method on document, or if you have a card that's expired, you will possibly not have the ability to download apps. This may also business lead to a Confirmation Required pop-up message. Get yourself a valid payment method on document and you may be able to begin downloading applications again.

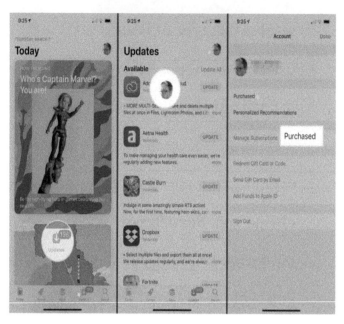

- Sign from the App Store and indication back. An iPhone that can't download applications may be considered an indication that something is up with your Apple ID. If the bond created by your Apple ID in the middle of your iPhone and the App Store gets disrupted, sometimes simply putting your signature on out and putting your signature on back will correct it. To achieve that, touch Configurations > iTunes & App Store > Apple ID > Indication Out. Then, indication back by tapping

82

Register and getting into your Apple ID account.

- Upgrade iOS. Whenever Apple produces an upgrade to the iOS - the operating-system that works on the iPhone, iPad, and iPod itouch - the new software fixes pests. Maybe your iPhone can't download applications due to an insect in the operating-system. A straightforward, fast, and free Operating-system revise may solve your trouble.

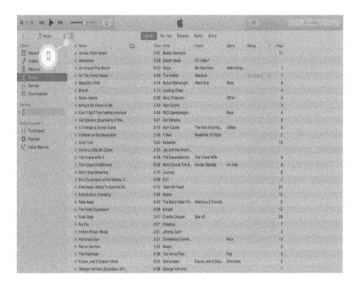

- Set correct day and time. Contrary to popular belief, but the time and time configurations on your mobile phone being incorrect can stop you

83

from downloading apps. The simplest way to resolve this is to make your iPhone automatically arranged its day and time so that it is always correct. To achieve that, tap Configurations > General > Day & Time > move the Arranged Automatically slider on/green.

- Reset iPhone device configurations. Bugs like applications not installing on your iPhone can often be the effect of a small problem in your low-level configurations. You can't always see these configurations or fix them separately, however the iOS provides you ways to reset all configurations. Accomplishing this won't erase your computer data, but can solve these kinds of issues.

• Check the Apple ID you're using. If you are creating a problem upgrading an application already on your device, the problem may be the Apple ID you're using. When you download an app, it's linked with the Apple ID you're logged into at that time. In the event that you change the Apple ID you're using, applications linked with the old ID will not be able to upgrade. Try putting your signature on into other Apple IDs you've used, following an instruction in step 7 above.

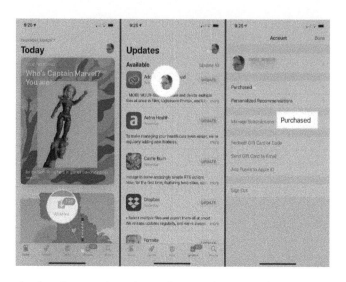

- Get help from Apple. If you have tried many of these steps as well as your iPhone still won't download apps, you will need help from professionals at Apple. You may get online or telephone support via Apple's website or you may make a scheduled appointment at the Genius Pub at your neighborhood Apple Store for in-person help.

How To Repair An iPhone That Is Unable To Update Apps

Ever come across a situation where your iPhone can't

update apps? It's uncommon, but it may also be a pretty complicated situation, especially because upgrading applications on your iPhone is usually as easy as tapping a few buttons. There are a lot of ways to resolve this problem, however the fixes aren't apparent. In case your iPhone won't upgrade apps and you understand your web connection is working fine (because you can't download applications without that!), I'm assuring you that you're reading the right book for the solution. This book has 12 methods for getting your iPhone upgrading apps again.

1 Restart iPhone

A straightforward step that can solve many iPhone problems is restarting these devices. Sometimes your mobile phone just must be reset. When it begins fresh, things that didn't work before instantly do, including upgrading apps. To restart your iPhone:

- Keep down the rest/wake (or Part) button.

- When the slider shows up near the top of the display screen, move it from remaining to right.

- Allow iPhone switch off.

- If it is off, keep down the rest/wake button again before Apple logo shows up.

- Forget about the button and allow phone set up as normal.

2 Pause and Restart the App Download

A problem downloading an application may also be caused by the bond between your telephone and the App Store getting interrupted. You are able to reset that connection by pausing the download and restarting it. This program is a little concealed, but here's where to find it:

- Find the icon your "home screen" for the application that you're wanting to download.

- Tap and keep it (on devices with 3D Touch

displays, press hard onto it).

- In the menu that pops out, faucet Pause Download.

- Wait an instant, then touch the application icon again to resume the download.

3 Update to the most recent Version of iOS

Another common solution to numerous problems is to ensure you're operating the latest version of the iOS. That is especially important when you can't revise apps, since improvements to apps may need a more recent version of the iOS than you have.

Methods for Wirelessly Editing iOS on an iPhone

Each new version of iOS-the operating-system that runs the iPhone-brings new features, bug fixes, and changes from what the telephone can do and exactly how it's used. Improving to a fresh version of iOS used to involve linking the iOS device to a Personal computer, downloading the upgrade to the computer, then setting up the revise by syncing with iTunes. Nowadays, iOS improvements can be installed wirelessly (a method known as over-the-air, or OTA, upgrading).

How to Upgrade iOS Wirelessly on the iPhone

Before you start an update:

- Back up your computer data to iCloud or iTunes should in case something goes wrongly with the update and the telephone must be restored.

- Hook up to a Wi-Fi network. The upgrade can be downloaded more than a mobile network; however, the improvements are large (often 1GB or even more), might take quite a while to download, and use your regular monthly cellular data. Wi-Fi is simpler and faster.

- Charge the iPhone electric battery. The download and set up process does take time. If there's significantly less than 50 percent electric battery life staying, charge the electric battery before the revise.

To upgrade iOS:

- For the iPhone Home display, tap the Configurations app.

- Scroll down, then faucet General.

- Tap Software Revise. The device investigations to find out if there's a revise. When there is, it reviews what it is and the actual upgrade increases the device.

- Touch Download and Install to start setting up the iPhone software revise.

- If the telephone is shielded with a passcode, enter the passcode to start the download. A blue improvement bar moves over the screen.

- Touch Install Now. The display screen will go dark, then shows the Apple logo. An improvement pub shows the position of the upgrade. When the iOS revise coatings, the iPhone restarts and shows a conclusion notice.

Tricks for iOS Upgrade

The iPhone notifies you when there's an update even though you don't look for it. If you visit a red 1 icon the Configurations application on your home display, which means there's an iOS upgrade available. You may even receive a force notification.

If there is not enough empty space for storage available on these devices to set up the update, understand how to update iPhone when you do not have enough space and follow the tips to repair this situation.

If something goes wrongly with the installation, there are two options to repair it: Recovery Setting or (if things go badly) DFU Setting. Another consequence of a failed update is a white display screen of death.

How To Get The Latest iOS Updates And Install Them

When Apple produces a fresh update to iOS - the operating-system that works the iPhone, iPod itouch, and iPad - set it up. Updates to iOS deliver insect fixes, user interface tweaks, and new features. Update to the latest version of the iOS in two ways: through iTunes or on the iPhone. To revise on the iPhone, see how to upgrade iOS wirelessly on the iPhone. Here's how to execute the revise using iTunes on macOS and Home windows computers.

How to Upgrade iOS Using iTunes

Using iTunes to upgrade your iPhone or iPad is an

excellent option if your iOS device is low on space. Follow these steps to keep the device current even whether it's full.

- Connect the iOS device to the computer you sync it with and release iTunes.

- Click on the icon for your device to open up these devices' management screen.

- Click Sync or **Backup** Now to either sync these devices with the computer or produce a back-up of the info on the telephone. It's good to truly have a back-up in the event anything goes incorrect with the upgrade.

- Click Sync or **Support** Now to either sync these devices with the computer or develop a back-up of the info on the telephone. It's good to truly have a back-up should in case anything goes wrong with the update.

- When the sync is complete, the iPhone

management display shows the version of iOS on these devices and information in regards to a newer version if the first is available. Click Revise to start the process.

- Click Download And then download the program for a later revise or click Download and Install to upgrade now.

- Browse the information about new features, fixes, and changes the new version of the iOS offers, then click Next.

- Click Consent to acknowledge an individual agreement.

- The revise downloads and automatically installs on your device. If prompted, follow the instructions.

- When the set-up is complete, these devices will automatically restart.

4 Ensure that You're Using the appropriate Apple ID

If you cannot update apps, start by confirming if you are using the right Apple ID. When you download an app, it's linked with the Apple ID you used when you downloaded it. Which means that you'll require to be logged into that original Apple ID to use the application on your iPhone.

On your own iPhone, check what Apple ID was used to get an application by following these steps:

- Touch the App Store app.

- Tap Updates.

- Touch your picture or icon in the very best right part (skip this task in iOS 10 or previously).

- Tap Purchased.

- Determine if the application is right here. If not, it was likely downloaded with another Apple ID.

If you are using iTunes (and are owning a version that still shows your apps; iTunes 12.7 removed the App Store and apps), you can confirm what Apple ID was used to get an application by following these steps:

- Head to your set of apps.

- Right-click the application you have in mind.

- Click Get Info.

- Click the Document tab.

- Take a look at Purchased by for the Apple ID.

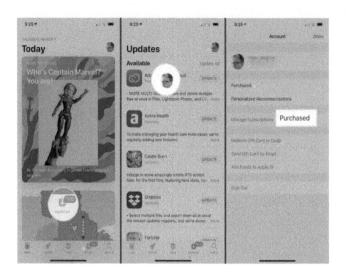

If you used another Apple ID before, try logging into that person's account to find out if it fixes your problem (Settings -> iTunes & App Stores -> Apple ID).

5 Ensure Restrictions Are Off

The Limitations feature of the iOS is, by iOS 12, situated in the Display Time settings. It enables people (usually parents or corporate and business IT administrators) disable certain top features of the iPhone. One particular feature is the capability to download apps. So, if you cannot install an upgrade, the feature may be blocked.

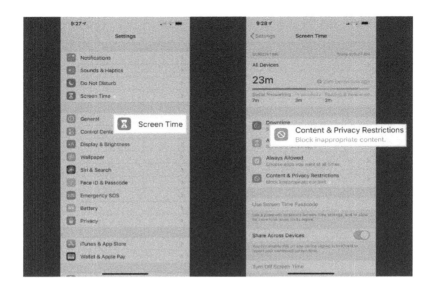

To check on this or switch off app limitations, follow these steps:

- Tap Settings.

- Tap Display screen Time.

- Touch Content & Personal privacy Restrictions.

- Tap Content Limitations.

- Tap Apps. Be certain that All Apps is examined.

In previous versions of the iOS, Restrictions are positioned in Settings -> General -> Restrictions.

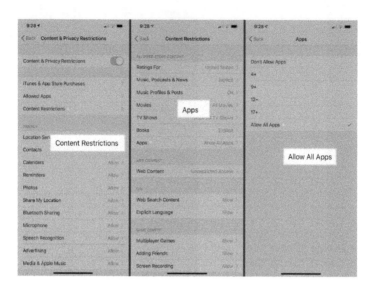

6 Sign Out And Back To The App Store

Sometimes, all you have to do to repair an iPhone that can't revise applications is to sign in and out of your Apple ID. It's simple, but that can solve the problem. Some tips about what you must do:

- Tap Settings.
- Touch iTunes & App Store.
- Touch the Apple ID menu (it lists the e-mail address you utilize for your Apple ID).
- In the pop-up menu, faucet Sign Out.

- Touch the Apple ID menu again and register with your Apple ID.

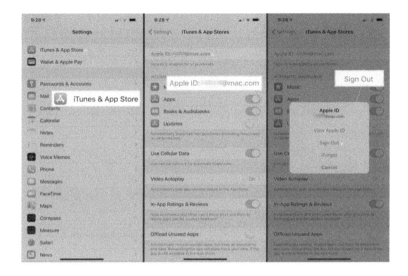

7 Check Available Storage

Here is a simple description: Perhaps you can't install the application update because you do not have enough available space for storage on your iPhone. If you very, hardly any free storage, the telephone might not have the area it requires to execute the upgrade and easily fit into the new version of the app.

Check your free space for storage by pursuing these

steps:

- Tap Settings.

- Tap General.

- Tap About.

- Search for the Available collection. That's how much free space you have.

In case your available storage space is surprisingly low, try deleting some data that's not necessary like apps, photos, podcasts, or videos.

8. Change Day and Time Setting

Your iPhone's day and time settings influence whether it can update apps. The reason why because of this are complicated, but essentially, your iPhone performs lots of inspections when interacting with Apple's servers to do things such as update apps. One particular check is perfect for time. In case your configurations are wrong, it can prevent you from having the ability to update apps.

To solve this issue, set your day and time for you to automatically update your apps by following these steps:

- Tap Settings.

- Tap General.

- Tap Time & Time.

- Move the Arranged Automatically slider to on/green.

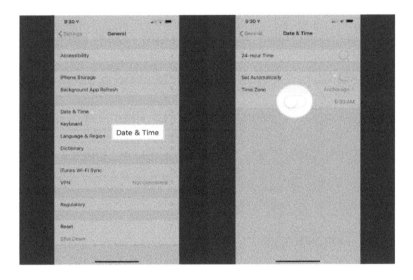

9 Delete and Reinstall the App

If nothing at all else spent some time working up to now, try deleting and reinstalling the app. Sometimes an application just requires a fresh start so when you do that, you'll install the latest version of the app.

10 Reset All Settings

Should in case you still can't update apps, you may want to try slightly more drastic steps to get things working again. The first option here's to try resetting your iPhone's configurations.

This won't delete any data from your phone. It just reverts a few of your requirements and settings with their original says. You can transform them back again after your applications are upgrading again. Here's how to do it:

- Tap Settings.
- Tap General.
- Tap Reset.
- Touch Reset All Configurations.
- You might be asked to enter your passcode. If

you're, do so.

- In the pop-up windows, touch Reset All Configurations.

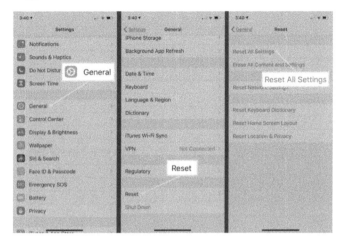

11 Update the App Using iTunes

If an application won't update on your iPhone, try carrying it out through iTunes (assuming you utilize iTunes with your telephone). Upgrading this way is fairly simple:

- On your pc, launch iTunes.
- Select Apps from the drop-down menu at the very top left.

- Click Updates underneath the top windowpane.

- Single-click the icon of the application you want to revise.

- In the section that starts, click the Upgrade button.

- When the application has up to date, sync your iPhone like normal and install the up to date app.

12 Bring back iPhone to Factory Settings

Lastly, if absolutely nothing else spent some time working, it is time to try the most drastic step of most: deleting from your iPhone and configuring it from scratch.

This is a larger process, so we have a complete article specialized in this issue: How exactly to Restore iPhone to Factory Configurations.

After that's done, you may even want to revive your iPhone from backup.

How to Print Using AirPrint From Your iPhone

Connect your phone or other Apple devices wirelessly to some printer. From your document, tap Share > Print > Select Printer under Printer Options > tap the inkjet printer you need > Print.

It is possible to connect your iPhone along with other Apple company devices to some printer to print files stored on your phone, iPad, and/or even iPod touch.

You need to be using an Airprint-supported app, linked to an Airprint-supported printer, and on a single Wi-Fi network.

How to Make use of AirPrint

To print the document with an iOS device making use of AirPrint:

- Open, the record, photo, email, or other files that

you would like to print.

- Tap Talk about, then tap Print out.

Note: When the Printing option isn't in the list, swipe to the bottom of the symbols to display even more options. If it's not with this checklist, the app might not support printing.

- In the Printer Options display, tap Select Printer.

- In the Printer display screen, tap an inkjet printer.

- Touch the + and - control keys to set the number of copies to printing.

Note: With regards to the printer, additional options may be obtainable, for instance, double-sided printing, color selection, and web page varies for multi-page files.

- When you have made your choices, faucet Print.

- The record will go directly to the printer.

Requirements for Making use of AirPrint

The iPhone does not have a USB port, and can't be connected to the printers with cables just like a desktop computer or laptop. Instead, it utilizes AirPrint. AirPrint is a wireless technology included in every iOS gadget that makes use of Wi-Fi and suitable printers to printing from your iPhone. To utilize AirPrint from an iOS gadget:

- Setup an AirPrint-compatible inkjet printer. Not absolutely all printers works with AirPrint, examine Apple's listing before you get.

- Link the iOS device and inkjet printer to the same Wi-Fi system. An iPhone linked to a functioning system cannot print to some printer linked to a home system, for example.

- Install an app that facilitates AirPrint around the iOS device.

Pre-Loaded iOS Apps That Support AirPrint

The next Apple-supported apps pre-loaded in the iPhone, iPad, and iPod iTouch that support AirPrint:

- Mail

- Maps

- Notes

- Photos

- Safari

Chapter 4

Advice For Setting Up An iPhone To Connect To Wi-Fi

To have the fastest web connection for your iPhone, hook up to Wi-Fi. With an iPod touch, the only path to get online is Wi-Fi since it generally does not support mobile data contacts. Wi-Fi is a high-speed cellular networking connection within homes, offices, espresso shops, restaurants, and other areas. Wi-Fi does not have the data limitations that telephone companies' monthly programs impose on mobile data use. Some Wi-Fi systems are private and security password protected (your office or home network, for example), although some are general public and open to anyone, either free of charge or a charge.

Methods for Setting Up an iPhone for WiFi

To get online using Wi-Fi with an iOS device such as an iPhone, iPod Touch, or iPad, follow these steps:

- From the house screen, faucet the Configurations app.
- Touch Wi-Fi, then start the Wi-Fi toggle change. A summary of all available systems shows up in the Select a Network section.
- Two types of Wi-Fi systems exist: open public and private. Private systems have a lock icon next to them, and general public ones don't. The pubs next to each network name show the effectiveness of the bond - the greater pubs, the faster the bond.

To become listed on a public network, touch the network's name. To become listed on an exclusive network, faucet the network's name, get into the security password, then tap Sign up for.

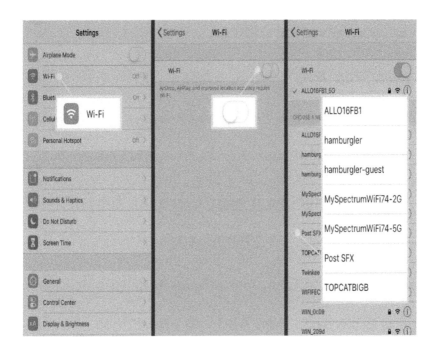

How to Use the Voice Memo App on an iPhone

Apple's Tone of voice Memos is a free of charge app that enables you to record sound on iPhone, iPad, and Apple Watch. This tone of voice recorder application includes an easy streamlined style with a basic report and edit features, it also help with the capability to export audio recordings to some other services for back-up, sharing, or even more advanced editing.

Notice: The Tone of voice Memos app arrives to set up on all iOS products, but if you've erased it, it is possible to reinstall it from your App Store free of charge.

How to Report on iPhone Using the Tone of voice Memos App

Recording audio using the iPhone Tone of voice Memos app is quite easy. Here's how to record tone of voice on iPhone.

- Open the Tone of voice Memos app on your iPhone or any iOS device.

- Touch the red report button at the bottom of the display to start voice recording afresh.

Note: Only a fast tap is okay. You don't have to hold it.

- Tap the tiny red horizontal collection for you to view more options regarding your document. In the display screen that opens, it is possible to pause the recording and continue it to help keep several recordings in the same sound file.

- Touch the red quit button when you wish to stop documenting.

- Select New record near the top of the display and type a name for that record. The record is saved beneath the name you type.

How to Cut a Tone of voice Memo in iPhone

Apple's Tone of voice Memos app includes just basic editing efficiency. Here's how to cut a voice recording in the app.

- Touch the audio record you intend to edit on the Voice Memos starting screen.

- Touch the ellipsis.

- Tap Edit Saving.

- Touch the crop icon.

- Pull the yellow deals at the bottom of the display screen to enclose the portion of the record you intend to keep.

- Tap Trim to eliminate any area of the saving outside the cut handles.

- Tap Save to verify the changes.

- To delete a portion of the sound, faucet the crop symbol, choose an area of the timeline and touch Delete. Finally, faucet Save.

- When you've finished making all your edits towards the audio file, touch Done.

How to Delete a good iPhone Tone of voice Memo

To delete a voice record in the Tone of voice Memos app, faucet the record, after that tap the garbage to close it.

You won't get a confirmation prompt, but if you accidentally delete a record, you may get it back. Touch the Lately Deleted category, touch the file's title, then faucet Recover > Recover Record.

How to Send Tone of voice Memos on iPhone

Once recorded, audio record in the Tone of voice Memos app could be delivered to a multitude of app.

- Tap the document you intend to send.

- Touch the ellipsis.

- Tap Share.

- Tap a get in touch to deliver it or export it for an app.

You can even scroll right down to backup the Apple Tone of voice Memo record with a cloud storage space service like Dropbox or even tap Save to Files to save lots of it for your device.

Note: If you experience any mistakes when exporting or even burning your recording, try to send it to yourself by an e-mail, open the document on your PC, and send it to your selected service or get in touch with following that.

The tone of voice Memos App Tips

The voice recorder in iPhone app, Tone of voice Memos, could be very helpful tool for conducting interviews or taking notes. You can also use it to record phone calls.

Below are a few useful ideas to get almost all from it.

Examine your storage: While Tone of voice Memos records can technically choose how long it will be, they are limited by the number of free of charge space on your device. If required, you can release some space.

Do a check documenting: Before performing a significant long-form interview, execute a fast 10-second check records to make sure that everything's operating fine in which background noise is completely filter.

Use a mic: You don't have to work with a mic, but linking someone to your iPhone may greatly enhance audio quality. Remember that you might need a dongle.

Backup your records instantly: Like a precaution, it's a good concept to e-mail yourself a duplicate of the tone of voice recording when it's done or back it up to cloud support like OneDrive or Search engines Drive. In this manner, your essential audio won't be lost if you lose or crack your iPhone.

Getting Rid of Podcasts on an iPhone

Podcasts are usually terrific, educational, entertaining methods to pass enough time, but they may also occupy plenty of space for storage on your iPhone. If you want to free up space, among the first things you can do would be to delete podcasts from your iPhone.

How to Delete Your Podcast Shows From iPhone

If you haven't paid attention to all the shows of the podcast you've downloaded, it is possible to take away the ones you've paid attention to without losing others.

To delete an individual podcast from your iPhone, adhere to these actions:

- Touch the Podcasts app to open up it.

- Ensure that the podcast show you intend to delete by visiting either the Pay attention Now tab or the Library tab.

- Make a brief swipe from left over in the episode you intend to remove and touch Delete. On the other hand, swipe completely across the display to delete the event right away.

Take note: *This just saves space if you delete podcasts you've currently downloaded. Podcasts using the download sign (the cloud having a down arrow in it) close to them, but haven't been able to download. Deleting them won't conserve space.*

How to Delete a whole Podcast Collection From iPhone

Is there any podcast you utilized to like, but don't pay attention to it anymore? Desire to delete the complete podcast from your iPhone, which includes all shows you've downloaded? Here's how:

- Using the Podcasts app open, tap Library, and locate the podcast you intend to delete.

- Tap the ... image close to a bout of the podcast.

- Touch Delete from Collection.

- In the pop-up, tap Delete from Library.

How to Automatically Delete Played Podcasts From iPhone

It is possible to set your Podcasts app to save lots of space by automatically deleting podcasts shows after you check them out. This can be a great way to save lots of space but enjoy your preferred displays. Here's how:

- Touch the App Settings to open it up.

- Tap Podcasts.

- Toggle the Delete Played Shows slider to on/natural.

Tips: Making use of these methods applies the delete-played-episodes environment to every podcast you sign up to. If you wish to have it use and then some podcasts, release the Podcasts app, that touch Library > the ... symbol > Settings.

How to Cease Auto Podcast Downloads in iPhone

When you initially registered to a podcast on your iPhone, you might have set the podcast to instantly download new shows. If you haven't paid attention to those shows, you might have an enormous backlog of podcasts taking on your space on your phone. To avoid podcasts from immediately downloading on your iPhone, stick to these ways:

- Touch the Podcasts app to open it up.

- Tap Library.

- Tap a bout of the podcast you intend to cease from automatically downloading shows.

- Tap the ... image.

- Tap Settings.

- Within the Custom section, tap Download Shows.

- Tap Off.

Suggestions: *Another good method to reduce the space your podcasts use up is to control the number of shows from anybody podcast series which are downloaded on your phone. To get this done, start the Podcasts app, after that tap Collection > the ... symbol > Configurations > Limit Shows. From there, pick the number of shows or date variety you want.*

Steps to Take When the iPhone App Stops

Functioning

The iPhone's app is easily among the most-used apps on Apple's smartphones, yet sometimes the telephone app freezes, keeps crashing, or simply stops working properly. Like tech problems can prevent you from making phone calls, receiving phone calls from relatives and buddies, and also from listening to calls whenever they come in.

How iPhone Mobile phone App Issues Appear

iPhone Cell phone app bugs may take various types. Occasionally the app will open through the iPhone's home display screen, while at various other times the telephone app will steadily continue to freeze rather than respond.

Phone calls may also be affected, having the ability to make outgoing calls or even receive incoming phone calls occasionally being handicapped. The default or custom made ringtones could also remain silent, and the specific appearance from the app could even look different.

Factors behind iPhone App Bugs

Bugs affecting the iOS phone app tend to be caused by the phone service provider or perhaps a conflict due to an app or even operating system update. The incorrect configurations being turned on or deactivated may also be behind mobile phone app issues. Fortunately, there are a variety of solution for such iPhone app issues.

How to Repair iPhone App Problems

If you're having troubles with your iPhone app, there are many things you can do to get it functioning perfectly again.

Close the iPhone app. Whenever the iPhone app freezes or halts working properly, closing the app and starting it again could repair the problem.

Note: Simply changing to some other app for your iPhone's home screen won't close up the phone app. You will need to swipe through to the display to close all your open apps and drag the phone app to close it correctly.

Restart your iPhone. Restarting can repair any bugs which are stopping the telephone app from functioning properly and may be considered a good answer whenever your Cell phone app keeps crashing. This technique can also help in any connection mistakes you might be having with your cellular provider.

Turn Airplane Setting off. If you've seen a film or have been flying, you might have forgotten to turn your iPhone's Aircraft Setting off. If on, this function will avoid you from receiving calls from anyone, and keep you from getting in touch with others.

Switch Airplane Setting on / off again. If you're having difficulty connecting your phone, try switching Airplane

Setting on, wait for 30 seconds, and switch it off once again. This can reset your link.

Turn on Cell phone Information. Swipe down in the top-right corner of your iPhone and be sure the Mobile Information icon is natural. If it's not really, tap it to carefully turn it on.

Verify your Bluetooth devices. If you're getting difficulty hearing calls, check all your Bluetooth loudspeakers and earphones, such as the Apple AirPods, to find out when the calls are increasingly being diverted in the speakers. If that is indeed the situation, you might try removing the gadgets from your iPhone or switching your iPhone's Bluetooth off entirely.

Are you utilizing the perfect app? If you suspect your iPhone app isn't working correctly or observe that it looks different all of a sudden, be sure you're utilizing the right app. Similar phone and messaging apps such as WhatsApp, WeChat, and other Communications apps have virtually identical green symbols to the main one utilized by the phone app.

Did you pay out your cellular bills? It's feasible that you will find a missed transaction and your cellular carrier has restricted your call features on your iPhone. Contact your supplier from another mobile phone or go to a branch to make sure that everything will be okay with your account.

Disable Do Not Disturb Setting. The Do Not Disturb setting continues to be regarded as the best option once the iPhone Mobile app freezes.

Reset Network Settings. This may get rid of any conflicting information which may be behind your damaged iPhone mobile app.

Update your iPhone. Along with adding new functions

and extra protection improvements, an iOS upgrade can also repair bugs and glitches which have been recognized by users as well as the developers.

Have you got a roaming strategy? If you're touring overseas and you're having difficulty making a phone call from your iPhone mobile app, it's achievable that you may not have worldwide roaming enabled on your smartphone.

Check out your SIM cards. If you've been using the same SIM card for some time, it may have finally been exhausted and be looking for replacing.

Reset your iPhone. This can reset your iPhone to its factory settings and present you with a brand new setup and interface.

Recover your iPhone. This will certainly be a final resort as it could bring about some data reduction. If you've attempted all other solutions on this list though, that is well worth attempting and is normally effective in repairing several iPhone problems.

Tips for Using Your iPhone's AssistiveTouch

Including an onscreen home button for your, iPhone could be great. It's your very best bet for keeping your iPhone operating if it includes a damaged home button. It is also crucial for those who have accessibility difficulties. And, it's an excellent shortcut for some helpful features. To include a Home switch, use a function known as AssistiveTouch on iPhone.

How Does AssistiveTouch Work?

AssistiveTouch places a virtual home button on your iPhone's display. This virtual home button lets you perform the same activities as pressing the home key, but by tapping an onscreen image instead. Also, it contains shortcuts to typical tasks that include the Home switch and lets you customize the shortcuts set off by tapping it.

AssistiveTouch was created for people who have physical conditions which makes it hard to allow them to push the button. Since that time, it has been used as a workaround for damaged Home control keys (for example, it can help repair an iPhone that will not switch off), by people who are concerned that the Home key will degrade if they click on it in an excessive way (that isn't true, incidentally), and by those that like the capability of the feature.

Ways to Position a Home Switch Using AssistiveTouch on Your iPhone Display

To add a home button for your iPhone screen simply by enabling AssistiveTouch, follow these measures:

- In iOS 13 or more tap Settings > Accessibility.

- If you are using iOS 12, head to Settings > General > Accessibility.

- Go to Contact > AssistiveTouch to get the button to carefully turn it on.

- If you are using iOS 12, simply tap AssistiveTouch through the Accessibility screen.

- On the AssistiveTouch screen, shift the slider to on/green.

- A new, icon, appears on your screen. That's your brand-new virtual onscreen home button.

How to Use the iPhone's AssistiveTouch feature

With AssistiveTouch touch fired up, here's how exactly to use it.

Tapping the icon introduces a menu with the next options:

Notifications: Provides fast access to Notification.

Custom: Enables you to access any custom made shortcuts or activities you've created.

Device: Gives one-touch access to normal features that include locking the telephone, raising and decreasing volume, mute, and much more.

Siri: Launches Siri (big shock, right?).

Control Middle: Reveals Handle Middle (another surprise).

Home: The same as clicking the home button. Similar to the bodily Home button, you can even double-tap it.

Once you select these options, it is possible to return by tapping the trunk arrow at the biggest market of the window.

You pull and fall the AssistiveTouch symbol to move around the display screen to a posture that's preferred or beneficial to you.

Tips for Personalizing iPhone's AssistiveTouch

Want to modify the actions which are triggered once you touch or double faucet the AssistiveTouch on-screen home button? It is possible to. Just adhere to these tips:

- In iOS 13 or more, head to Settings > Accessibility > Contact > AssistiveTouch.

- In iOS 12, head to Settings > Common > Convenience > AssistiveTouch.

It is possible to control what goes on to get a Single-Tap, Double-Tap, or even Long Press. Touch the menu at the action you intend to customize.

Select the actions you want in the available list.

For Double-Tap and Long Press, you can even control the number of times necessary for the actions before it's time out. Handle this in the Double-Tap Timeout and Long Push Duration selections, respectively.

How to Turn Off iPhone AssistiveTouch

Don't need your onscreen home button anymore? Switch off AssistiveTouch by following these actions:

- In iOS 13 or more, tap Settings > Accessibility > Contact > AssistiveTouch.

- If you are using iOS 12, head to Settings > General > Accessibility > AssistiveTouch.

- Proceed the AssistiveTouch slider to off/white.

Chapter 5

Making a "Hey Siri" Shortcut on an iPhone

The Shortcuts feature in iOS automates both fundamental and complex tasks to save lots of time and help to make your phone usage better. Along with producing your personal 'Hey Siri, I'm obtaining drawn over' shortcuts, it is possible to download ready-made shortcuts from the web.

One pre-programmed shortcut shows up thanks to Robert Petersen, who created it to greatly help people protect themselves during encounters with the authorities. Here are what it can and ways to get it.

What Will the 'I'm Finding Pulled Over' Shortcut Carry out?

As soon as you activate this shortcut, your cell phone performs the next actions:

- Activates Usually Do Not Disturb, which converts off all notifications for inbound calls and communications.

- Sets the display brightness to no.

- Sends a text to some selected connection with where you are in Apple company Maps.

- Starts recording the video from your front (selfie) digital camera.

After you quit documenting, your phone will:

- Turn off Usually Do Not Disturb.

- Save the movie in your Recent folder in Photos and deliver a copy to the recipients you designate.

- Prompt you to upload the movie to iCloud Generate or Dropbox.

How to Take the 'I'm Getting Drawn More than' Shortcut

Before you use Petersen's plan, you need to inform your iPhone to permit "untrusted" shortcuts. These macros are usually ones that you will get from the web instead of in the Shortcuts app. To regulate this setting, open up the Configurations app, go for Shortcuts, and tap the change close to Allow Untrusted Shortcuts to on/natural.

Now, you're prepared to set up the "I'm Obtaining Stopped" shortcut. Some tips about what to accomplish.:

- Go directly to the Shortcut's guide on Reddit to discover an URL to the most present version.

- Open that hyperlink using Safari on your iPhone.

- Tap Find Shortcut.

- The Shortcuts app will open, and you will see a set of everything it can. Scroll right down to evaluate most of its features.

- At the bottom of the web page, tap Add Untrusted Shortcut.

- In the next stage, choose more recipients. Individuals you choose right here will receive a copy of the movie you take. It is possible to select the same recipients as in the last action or different styles. Tap Done to complete setting up.

- You'll go back to the Gallery page from the Shortcuts app.

- You might still have to give some permissions before the shortcut will continue to work properly. To start, open the Configurations app.

- Select Shortcuts.

- Tap Location.

- Chose the degree of permission you intend to offer the Shortcuts app. To save lots of time if you are operating on the shortcut, selected With all the

App.

- Go back to the Shortcuts app and make sure you're on *My Shortcuts tabs*.

- Tap the greater (three dots) menu in the upper-right part from the I'm obtaining stopped shortcut.

- Scroll right down to Camera and faucet Allow Access.

- Tap OK in the small windows that open.

- Repeat Actions 15 and 16 for Photos and Communications.

- Automagically, this shortcut uses your front-facing camera, nevertheless, you can also select a various one. Tap the Front side under Camera and select Back if you'd like to use some other camera.

- Finally, scroll right down to the Scripting section to select where to upload your video by the end of the shortcut. Automagically, you should use iCloud

140

Push, Dropbox, or perhaps a "Usually do not upload" choice. Touch the minus switch and Delete to eliminate several options.

- Select Done to save lots of your settings.

To run this program, possibly open up the Shortcuts app and touch its button in the *My Shortcuts display screen*, or even activate Siri and state, "I'm getting stopped."

How to Transfer Music Between iPhones

Drifting regularly between 2 iPhones or just desire to send music to some other device, like an adored one's iPhone? You can find multiple ways to share songs with some other iPhone that may be complicated when all you have to do will be share some preferred tracks with somebody.

Methods for Downloading Music to an iPhone Using Apple Music

If you sign up for Apple Music, it's incredibly easy to download songs to another iPhone or exchange everything via the Apple Music design feature that allows you to utilize Apple Music across several devices via the same account. To take action, you require to carefully turn on Sync Collection to access your songs library. Here's how to set points up.

- On your main iPhone, tap Settings.

- Scroll straight down and tap Songs.

- Tap Sync Collection toggle it about.

Your songs will now sync across to any iPhones which are signed in on a single account. You don't need to do other things for you to start seeing the music.

How to Transfer Music Across iPhones Utilizing Household Sharing

If you wish to talk about songs (or other documents) in the middle of your iPhones and they are all on the same Wi-Fi network, you should use an attribute called Home Sharing to create it probably. It's obtainable through iTunes permitting around five computers in your household in addition to all of your iOS products and Apple Televisions to share content material. This method is usually ideal if you to want to talk about other files such as photos with gadgets such as your home's Apple TV. Here's how to arrange it in the middle of your iPhones making use of your Mac like a go-between.

- On your own Mac, click on the Apple icon.

- Click System Choices.

- Click Sharing.

- Click Media Posting.

- Click Home Revealing.

- Sign in with your Apple ID and click on Turn On Home Sharing.

Now that Home Sharing is turned on across all of your devices on a single Wi-Fi network, it's easy to use on your iPhone. Some tips on what to do.

- On your own iPhone, tap Music.

- Tap Library.

- Tap Home Spreading.

At this point, you have access to the home Sharing Library of music any moment you're linked to the same Wi-Fi network.

Using AirDrop to Transfer Music Across iPhones

AirDrop can be an often forgotten basic method of transferring songs between any Mac PC or iOS gadget. Impressively, it works for moving music, it also requires seconds. Some tips about what to do.

- On the iPhone, tap Music.

- Find the track you intend to transfer.

- Tap the 3 dots icon.

- Tap Share.

- Tap AirDrop.

- Touch the iPhone you intend to deliver it to.

Four Ways To Fix iTunes Purchase Problems

Buying a track, book, or movie from the iTunes Store is usually simple and worry-free, but sometimes there are issues with your iTunes buys.

Problems happen for many reasons, but if you lose your web connection through the purchase or download, or there's one on Apple's part, you can finish up spending money on something however, not having the ability to download or play it. A number of the common issues that happen in these circumstances include:

- iTunes says that it's bought but it cannot be downloaded.

- A partly downloaded document that cannot be performed or used.

- Your credit cards are charged, nevertheless, you can't download.

- A document that seems to have completely downloaded, but doesn't play.

- A failed purchase.

If you are facing one of the above listed problems, here are 4 actions you can take to get this content you payed for from iTunes.

1. How To Proceed If iTunes Purchase Didn't Happen

The easiest kind of iTunes purchase problem to resolve is

if the transaction simply wasn't completed. If so, you merely need to choose the item again. You can examine to ensure the purchase didn't happen using iTunes by pursuing these steps:

- Open iTunes.
- Click the Accounts menu.
- Click View My Accounts.
- If you are asked to get your Apple ID accounts, do this and click *Register.*
- Scroll right down to the Purchase Background section.
- Click See All.
- Here, you can see whenever your latest purchase was and what it was. If that you just attempted to buy isn't outlined, your purchase failed and you will need to try again.

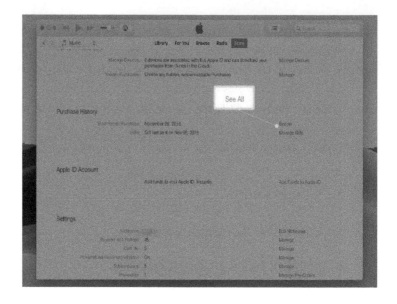

You can even check your purchases using the iTunes Store or App Store applications with an iOS device:

- Touch the application for the type of purchase you're looking at, either iTunes Store or App Store.

- In the App Store, touch your profile icon in the top right, then Purchased.

- Next, faucet My Purchases. When you have Family Posting set up, touch on the average person relative whose buys you want to check on.

- You are able to tap Not upon this iPhone near the

top of the app. This shows purchases not presently installed on your device.

- In the iTunes Store app, faucet the More tabs in the bottom, then Purchased. Touch Music, Films, or Television Shows to start to see the item you bought. When you have Family Writing, you can touch the individuals in your loved one's group below.

In both cases, if what you wanted to buy isn't listed, you weren't charged for this and the purchase didn't happen. Just return to the iTunes or App Store and purchase it as if you normally would.

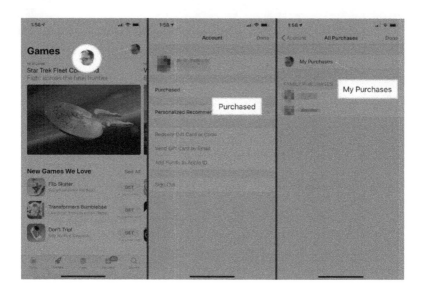

2. Look for Available Downloads in iTunes

In some instances, you may come across a download that starts and then stalls out before it completes. If that's the problem you're facing, you ought to be in a position to restart the download easily by following these steps:

- Open iTunes.

- Click the Accounts menu.

- Click Look for Available Downloads.

- If you are asked to enter your Apple ID, achieve this, then click Check.

- When you have a purchase that didn't download whatsoever or was interrupted, it will begin to download.

3. Redownload iTunes Buys Using iCloud

In case your purchase succeeded however the item you are considering doesn't appear when you follow the steps from the last section to check on for downloads, there's a straightforward solution so you can get your missing content: iCloud. Apple stores all your iTunes and App Store buys in your iCloud accounts where you can simply redownload them.

4. Ways to get iTunes Support From Apple

The first three options in this specific book should solve most iTunes purchase problems. However, if you are one of the unlucky few who's still got a problem even after attempting them, you have two options:

- Get active support from Apple's iTunes support

team. For step-by-step instructions about how to achieve that, read this book on requesting support from the iTunes Store.

- Use Apple's online help site to look for the best kind of support for you. This web site will ask you some questions about your problem and, predicated on your answers, offer an article to learn, a person to speak to, or lots to call.

How to Handle an Unrecognized iPhone with iTunes

Once you can't play your favorite songs, these solutions might help. iTunes is Apple's amusement hub, storing all of your songs, movies, Television shows, and much more. To take pleasure from iTunes across all of your devices, Apple enables you to sync iTunes on your PC and iPhone utilizing a USB link. While this generally works well, occasionally iTunes doesn't identify your iPhone, which may be frustrating and complicated.

Take a look at why this issue may occur and how exactly to repair it and get iPhone and iTunes in sync again.

Notice: With macOS Catalina, Apple company Music changed iTunes. These troubleshooting methods apply to techniques with old iTunes versions in addition to newer techniques with Apple Songs.

Factors behind iTunes Not Recognizing iPhone

There are many explanations why iTunes doesn't recognize an iPhone. There could be a physical problem, like a faulty USB wire or USB slot using the PC. Particles may clog the iPhone interface, or there may be a software issue.

Whatever the way may be to solve the issue, there are a few quick troubleshooting steps with a higher potential for getting an iPhone and iTunes back again.

How to correct it when itunes won't recognize your

iphone

Often, iPhone-to-iTunes connectivity problems stem from issues it is possible to fix. Attempt each troubleshooting phase to find out if it solves the issue. If it generally does not, move on to another suggestion.

Make sure iTunes is set up using the PC. Unless you have iTunes, this program can't understand the device. You can set up iTunes (or its successor, Apple company Music) on the Mac or Home windows PC.

Examine the USB wire. A faulty USB wire might lead to the iPhone-to-iTunes link issue. Make sure the USB wire is in good condition. Whether it's frayed or slice, use various USB cable and find out if this solves the issue.

Verify the iPhone's slot. Sometimes, debris accumulation leads to an iPhone interface to fail. Work with a dried out, anti-static clean or toothbrush to completely clean it out softly. Then, connect once again and find out if this fixes the problem.

Check out the USB slot using the PC. Start by unplugging all USB products from the PC. Proceed to the iPhone's wire to another interface and reconnect. If this functions, there's a problem with the specific port, and you will need to repair.

Restart the iPhone. A little software glitch might lead to a faulty link. Restart these devices and connect once again.

Restart the computer. A moderate software insect or breakdown could cause iTunes to breakdown. Switch off the PC and leave it for a couple of minutes before switching it back on again.

Make sure the iOS device is be unlocked and on the home screen. Connect these devices, instantly unlock it, and make sure it's on the home screen. Then link your iPhone to iTunes.

Download the most recent edition of iTunes. A vintage edition of iTunes might not acknowledge your iPhone. Upgrade iTunes and attempt to link the iPhone once again.

Update operating-system software. Update Home windows or macOS and find out if this manages any software program glitches or concealed bugs that triggered the iPhone-to-iTunes link problem.

Check the machine Report. This just applies if you are using a Mac PC. Connect the iPhone and check out the System Statement, which shows energetic devices. In case your iPhone is displayed, nevertheless, you can't link, you may be experiencing a software program issue.

Disable or uninstall security software. If you are using a Mac as well as the iPhone have been listed in the machine Record, disable or uninstall antivirus software program and other protection programs individually. Find out if any system causes the issue.

Reinstall the Apple company Mobile Gadget USB driver. This driver informs the PC how to proceed with Apple gadgets. When it malfunctions, it generally does not read the gadget properly. Reinstall the car owner and find out if this solves the issue.

Uninstall and reinstall iTunes. A breakdown of iTunes can often be solved by uninstalling and reinstalling the program.

Get in touch with Apple Help. The Apple company iTunes assistance website offers numerous helpful features, which includes a searchable understanding base and the capability to ask the city a question. You can even set up a scheduled appointment on the Genius Club of your nearby Apple Store.

Acknowledgments

The Glory of this book success goes to God Almighty and my beautiful Family, Fans, Readers & well-wishers, Customers and Friends for their endless support and encouragements.

Author Profile

Meet Chris Amber, the energetic writer behind "EnergyCyclist Publishing" who specializes in technology and gadget books. His love of dissecting the intricacies of modern technology has made him a respected authority in the area.

Background: Chris was eager to learn about the complex world of technology when he first started his adventure into it. Equipped with a technical studies degree, he immersed himself in the rapidly changing field of innovation, aiming to provide both enthusiasts and inquisitive minds with an understanding of the newest devices and technological breakthroughs.

Expertise: Chris has a deep understanding of the rapidly changing technology sector and focuses on producing incisive and easily understood material that helps users understand complicated technological ideas. His skill is not just in breaking down the technical nuances but also in turning them into captivating stories that appeal to a wide range of people.

Enthusiasm for Gadgets: Chris's passion for gadgets comes through in everything he writes. He enthusiastically navigates the fast-paced world of innovation, covering everything from wearables to smartphones to cutting-edge tech trends, making sure his readers stay educated and empowered in an era of rapid technological progress.

Highlights of Publications: Chris Amber is the author of several critically acclaimed books that explore various facets of technology and gadgets. His books are guides that lead readers on a thrilling voyage through the intriguing nexus of human life and technical growth, not just manuals.

Philosophy: Chris Amber is an advocate for universal access to technology. His writing style is centered on dissecting difficult ideas into manageable chunks so that his audience feels empowered and understood. In his view, technology is more than just a collection of devices; rather, it is a revolutionary force that is changing the way people interact with one another, live, and work.

Innovation Advocate: Chris regularly participates in the tech community outside of his writing career. He attends conferences and keeps up with the latest developments in technology. His dedication to staying current guarantees that his readers get the most up-to-date and pertinent information.

Chris Amber's books are portals to a future in which technology improves our lives rather than just being books about gadgets. Having a keen sense of creativity, Chris never stops motivating and educating others, which makes him a highly sought-after contributor to the field of technical writing.